© 1996 Geddes & Grosset Ltd

Reprinted 1997

Published by Geddes & Grosset Ltd,
New Lanark, Scotland.

ISBN 1 85534 178 6

Printed and bound in the UK

Starting School

Judy Hamilton
Illustrated by Beverley Sprio

Tarantula Books

The playground is very noisy this morning. Today, lots of boys and girls are starting school for the very first time.

Some children are very excited. They are running round in circles making a lot of noise.

But some children are very quiet. They are a little bit worried. What will school be like?

Louise is holding tightly onto her mother's hand. She is trying very hard not to cry.

"Don't worry," says her mother. "You will have a good time, just you wait and see."

The school bell rings. Everybody jumps!

The teacher comes out.

"Good morning, boys and girls," she says. "My name is Mrs Dunlop. Welcome to your new school. Come inside with me and I will show you where to hang your coats."

The grown-ups all go inside with the children. Mrs Dunlop shows the children the toilets for the boys and the toilets for the girls. Then she shows them the pegs in the cloakroom where they are to hang up their coats. She shows them the pictures above the pegs.

"Remember your picture, children," she says, "and you will remember where your peg is."

Hannah has a picture of an apple above her peg. Sam has a bear.

toilets

When the children have hung up their coats they follow Mrs Dunlop into the classroom. It is very bright and cheerful inside the classroom. There are lots of pictures on the wall and many things to look at.

Mrs Dunlop shows the children where they are to sit. Each child has a drawer in the table to keep his or her things in. Mrs Dunlop has made special name labels for the children to put on the table in front of them.

"This will help me to get to know you all very quickly," she says.

Louise feels more cheerful and smiles at her mother.

Now it is time for the grown-ups to leave. They kiss the children goodbye.

"Have a lovely time," they say, "and be good! See you at lunch time!"

Robert starts to cry when his mother goes away. Mrs Dunlop gives him a job to do, and he soon cheers up. He helps her to put a pot of coloured crayons on each table. Then Mrs Dunlop gives everybody a special notebook, which has the child's name written on the front.

"I want you all to draw a picture of yourselves in your notebooks," says Mrs Dunlop. "Use lots of bright colours!"

Louise

Soon, everyone is busy.

Mrs Dunlop goes round the tables, admiring the children's pictures. Sometimes she has to give a little help as well.

When all the pictures have been finished, Mrs Dunlop shows the children how to put their notebooks away neatly in their drawers.

"You have all worked hard and drawn beautiful pictures," she says. "Now you can choose something else to do for a while. You can paint at the painting table, or you can make a model at the gluing table, or you can look at books in the quiet corner."

She helps the children to choose and shows them what to do.

Ghita

Hannah and Robert have chosen to make a model, and they are working with each other, sticking boxes together to make a castle.

Ghita is painting a big red and blue flower

Sam and Louise look at books.

There is a knock at the door, and a man comes in carrying a big box.

"Boys and girls," says Mrs Dunlop, "Mr Jackson, the Janitor, has brought the milk for break time. Will you please say good morning to him?"

"Good morning, Mr Jackson," say the boys and girls.

"Good morning, boys and girls," says Mr Jackson.

"Now, boys and girls," says Mrs Dunlop, "Tidy up your things carefully. It will soon be time for break."

The paintbrushes are washed, and the paintings are put aside to dry. The books are put back on the bookshelves. The models are put on another shelf, ready to be taken home. Then Mrs Dunlop helps the children to look in their schoolbags to see what they have brought to eat at morning break. Ghita has brought an apple. Hannah's mum has packed a bag of crisps for her to eat.

Then Mrs Dunlop starts to hand round the cartons of milk.

Ghita looks worried. "I don't like milk," she says.

Mrs Dunlop smiles.

"That's all right, Ghita, " she says. "Your mother told me that you don't like milk, so we did not order a carton for you. You can get a drink of water from the drinking fountain if you feel thirsty."

When the children have eaten their snack and drunk all their milk, they all line up at the classroom door. Mrs Dunlop puts her finger to her lips.

"Ssh," she says. "When you are all nice and quiet, you may go outside to play in the playground for a little while."

At once, everybody is quiet!

Outside in the playground, the children run around excitedly. They play chasing games and make friends with each other. They watch some of the older children, who are playing football.

"I'm going to ask Mrs Dunlop if I can bring my football to school tomorrow," says Robert.

Soon, the school bell rings again. Mrs Dunlop comes out and shows the children where to line up quietly, ready to go inside again.

"This is where you will line up in the morning before school every day," she tells them.

When the children are gathered together in a nice quiet line, she leads them all inside.

Inside the classroom, Mrs Dunlop gives the children at each table a different job to do. The children at Hannah's table are going to do some sorting. Mrs Dunlop gives them lots of blocks of different colours. They have to sort them into piles, one for each colour.

The children at Robert's table are going to do some writing. Mrs Dunlop shows them how to write a nice, round, curly "c" and gives them pencils and paper to practise writing on.

The children at Ghita's table are going to do some reading. Mrs Dunlop sits with them and helps them to look at the pictures and tell the story in the book.

The children have all been working very hard. Mrs Dunlop is very pleased with them.

"Well done, everybody," she says. "Let's give ourselves a reward and do some singing now."

Mrs Dunlop gets out her guitar and sings a funny song to the children. It isn't hard to learn, and soon they are all joining in, singing loudly.

"What a lot of good singers I have in my class!" says Mrs Dunlop.

When the singing is finished, all the children sit down on the mat in front of Mrs Dunlop's desk, and she reads them a story. They all listen quietly. Sam and Robert suck their thumbs as they listen.

The school bell rings once more.

"It is time for you to go home now, boys and girls," says Mrs Dunlop. "Tuck your chairs neatly into the tables, please. Gather up your belongings and put them into your bags. Then line up quietly, and we will go and get your coats."

The children are all quiet as they fasten their coats. They have had a busy day and they are quite tired. One by one, they go out into the playground where the grown-ups are waiting to meet them.

"How was your first day at school?" says Hannah's mum.

"It was good," says Hannah. "What's for lunch? I'm *starving*!"